Jim S<

Straightforward Pre-intermediate
PORTFOLIO

Contents

Welcome to your *Straightforward* Pre-intermediate Portfolio

Me

Describe yourself

Write a description of yourself. Use some of the phrases in the box.

Stick your photo here.

> My name's …
> I live …
> I was born …
> I want to …
> Next year I …
> My home …
> I'm _____ years old.
> I have _____ sisters and _____ brothers.

_____
_____
_____
_____
_____
_____
_____
_____
_____
_____
_____

My favourite

Write your favourites.

transport

sport

job

book or film

song

place

restaurant

weather

way of wasting time

meal

time of year

clothes

My choices

Circle the correct words and phrases for you.

sleep late or get up early?

work or pretend to work?

do some sport or play a computer game?

bath or shower?

pasta or rice?

coffee or tea?

read a book or watch a movie?

chocolate or chips?

Language passport

My school/college

I go/went to _____.

The teacher who helped me most was my _____ teacher.

He/She _____.

School subjects
Number these school subjects in the order you liked best at school.

- ☐ mathematics
- ☐ science & technology
- ☐ geography
- ☐ history
- ☐ languages
- ☐ sport
- ☐ art

I hope I'll never have another lesson on _____.

The most useful subject I ever studied was _____.

I have passed these examinations:

I have the following qualifications:

Things I have learnt outside school:

I have these experiences of other cultures:

My languages

My mother tongue is _____.

What languages can you speak? Complete the table. (1 = just a little, 5 = fluently)

Language:	_____	_____	_____	_____
Speaking	1 2 3 4 5	1 2 3 4 5	1 2 3 4 5	1 2 3 4 5
Writing	1 2 3 4 5	1 2 3 4 5	1 2 3 4 5	1 2 3 4 5
Listening	1 2 3 4 5	1 2 3 4 5	1 2 3 4 5	1 2 3 4 5
Reading	1 2 3 4 5	1 2 3 4 5	1 2 3 4 5	1 2 3 4 5
Number of years studied				

These languages would be useful for me to learn in the future:

_____

Circle the best phrase to complete the sentences for you.

I find it very easy / quite easy / quite difficult / very difficult to learn a language.

I think that the most important thing in learning a language is to be able to speak / listen / read / write in the new language.

The most difficult thing for me is speaking / listening / reading / writing.

I would like to improve my pronunciation / spelling / vocabulary / grammar / fluency.

My English

I can do these things easily in English:

I can also do these things in English, but not easily:

These things are still very difficult for me:

I would really like to be able to do these things in English:

If you learn a new language, you get a new soul.

Czech proverb

My grammar

The following grammar items are studied at Common European Framework levels A1 to A2. How confident do you feel about your own understanding and use of each one? (1 = I don't know this very well. 2 = I know this fairly well. 3 = I have few problems with this.)

Grammar item	For example	1	2	3
A/an	a cat, an exercise			
Regular & irregular plurals	windows, women			
Verb to be – affirmative	I am, he is			
Possessive adjectives	his, their			
This, that, these, those	that hat, these books			
Present simple affirmative	She works at home.			
Present simple negative	She doesn't work at home.			
Present simple questions & short answers	Does she work at home? Yes, she does.			
Wh- questions	Where does she work?			
Possessive 's	Jim's car, the child's book			
Adjectives	tall, tired, tasty			
Prepositions of place	at, next to, opposite			
There is / there are	There are three boxes.			
How much/many	How much oil? How many pages?			
Some & any	Have you got any eggs?			
Prepositions of time	at ten o'clock, in winter, on Thursday			
Frequency adverbs	often, rarely, sometimes			
Can/can't	She can swim. He can't.			
Past simple was/were	They were late. She was kind.			
Past simple regular verbs	walked, wanted, watched			
Past simple irregular verbs	ate, went, saw			
Past time expressions	yesterday, last week, three weeks ago			
Adverbs of manner	slowly, angrily, easily			
A lot, not much, not enough	not much cheese, not enough water			
Too	too hot to drink, too heavy to carry			
verb + -ing	like walking, enjoy swimming			
Present continuous	She's working. We're cooking.			
Should/shouldn't	You should go home.			
Imperatives	Stand up! Close your books!			
Whose	Whose bike is this?			
Possessive pronouns	mine, yours, theirs			
Must/mustn't/needn't	He mustn't go in. You needn't do that.			
Comparatives	Heidi's taller than Jeff.			
Superlatives	It's the best. It's the most expensive.			
Will & going to for prediction	He'll come late. It's going to rain.			
Going to future	I'm going to buy a DVD.			
Present perfect simple affirmative	I've been there. He's written a book.			
Present perfect simple negative	She hasn't done it.			
Present perfect simple questions	Have you ever seen this film?			

Needs analysis

English is important for me because _____ .

I will need English in the future to _____ .

Tick the boxes to show how important these things are for you.

	not	quite	very
			important
Describe people and things	☐	☐	☐
Tell a story	☐	☐	☐
Express opinions and discuss topics	☐	☐	☐
Participate in meetings	☐	☐	☐
Make presentations	☐	☐	☐
Socialize in English	☐	☐	☐
Reserve hotels or book tickets	☐	☐	☐
Order food in restaurants	☐	☐	☐
Receive visitors	☐	☐	☐
Read newspaper and magazine articles	☐	☐	☐
Make telephone calls	☐	☐	☐
Read business or technical texts	☐	☐	☐
Read for enjoyment	☐	☐	☐
Understand information on the internet	☐	☐	☐
Understand presentations	☐	☐	☐
Understand movies and TV programmes	☐	☐	☐
Write and read notes and memos	☐	☐	☐
Write and read emails	☐	☐	☐
Write and read personal letters	☐	☐	☐
Write and read business letters	☐	☐	☐
Pass an exam	☐	☐	☐

Which two or three are your priorities? Mark them with a *.

Diary

You will find diary sections throughout this Portfolio. These are for you to write your thoughts while you study the course. How you use it is up to you. You can answer the question or use the diary space to write down:

- your answer to other questions on the page.
- interesting things that happen during lessons or study time.
- important or useful things you learn during the course.
- thoughts about what you are learning and how you are studying.
- things that are easy or difficult for you.
- things that you enjoy or don't enjoy.
- conversations you have with teachers or other students.

Look at the sample diary entry from page 23 of this Portfolio. It gives you an idea of the kind of thing you could write.

You are a third of the way through *Straightforward* Pre-intermediate. How are you getting on? Do you feel your English is improving?

Yes, I think my English is better now. I like my teacher; she's very kind and explains if I don't understand grammar. I like the word lists at the end of each unit in the Student's Book. They help me to remember important words from the lessons.

I have three hours of English lessons every week. I think that this is not enough to improve quickly, but I do a lot of work on my own at home with the Workbook. I really enjoy having this Portfolio to look at and write in too. I take it with me everywhere I go. I often read it on the bus and it makes me smile and helps me to see exactly what I can do in English that I couldn't do a few months ago.

I never travel without my diary.
One should always have something
sensational to read in a train.

Oscar Wilde

1A | Family life

Can do (tick ✓)

- [ ] I can understand a description of a typical English family.
- [ ] I can ask and answer questions about families.
- [ ] I can talk about people who are important to me.
- [ ] I can use the present simple to ask questions.

Diary

You are starting *Straightforward* Pre-intermediate. What do you hope will be good about studying this course?

_____

_____

_____

_____

_____

_____

_____

_____

My family

Write some true endings for these sentences.

1   My family is _____

   _____.

2   I get on really well with my _____.

3   The funniest person in my family is _____.

If someone met your family for the first time, what would they say about them?

'That's my family tree!'

1B | Where are they now?

Can do (tick ✓)

- [ ] I can understand specific information in a conversation about a photograph.
- [ ] I can describe someone in a photograph.
- [ ] I can ask and answer questions about friends.
- [ ] I can use verb collocations to ask questions about friendship.

My friends

Write about one or more of these questions.

- Do you have a friend who always makes you laugh?
- Do you have a friend who always listens to you?
- What sort of people do you get on well with?

Find a lost friend

Complete the information about a friend you haven't
seen for a long time.

LOST FRIEND

Full name: _____

Age now: _____

School: _____

Year last seen: _____

Place last seen: _____

What do you miss about them?

What will you talk about if you meet again? _____

> *When the character of a man
> is not clear to you, look at his friends.*
> **Japanese proverb**

1c | Neighbours

Can do (tick ✓)

- [ ] I can understand the main points in a magazine article.
- [ ] I can ask and answer questions about neighbours.
- [ ] I can use *how* and *what* with other words to make questions.
- [ ] I can pronounce and understand the letters of the alphabet.

My neighbours

Write about one of these topics: neighbours I like; neighbours I have never met; things that annoy me about my neighbours.

Diary

How well do you know the other people in your English class?
What do you like about your lessons?

_____

_____

_____

_____

_____

_____

_____

_____

_____

Spelling & sounds

Think of at least six more words for each of these phonemes.

/eɪ/	/iː/	/e/
train	see	leg
late	green	men

> *Good fences make good neighbours.*
> **Robert Frost (American poet)**

1D | Making contact

Can do (tick ✓)

- ☐ I can understand and write down telephone numbers.
- ☐ I can understand answering machine messages.
- ☐ I can leave a message on an answering machine.
- ☐ I can find information in newspaper advertisements.

My phone calls

Do you use the phone a lot, a little or never?
Who have you phoned in the last two days?
Are there people you phone all the time? Do you
mainly make social phone calls or are they for work?

*'If I dialled a wrong number,
why did you answer?'*

Rearrange the words to make a question. Then answer the question.

you   phone   ever   was   the   had   best   What   call   ?

?

Remember!

Write three things you would like to remember from Unit 1 and say why they are important for you.

1 _____

2 _____

3 _____

2A | School days

Can do (tick✓)

- I can understand people talking about their schooldays.
- I can talk about my school and my favourite teacher.
- I can use adjectives with prepositions to talk about my schooldays.
- I can use the past simple to talk about my education.

School subjects

Which school subjects have been the most useful to you in your life? Which subjects are not taught in schools but should be? If you were a teacher, what would you enjoy teaching?

Diary

In what ways is this course different from courses you have taken before? Are you working in different ways? Are you learning faster?

_____

_____

_____

_____

_____

_____

_____

_____

Story

Can you make a very short story using these verbs in <u>exactly</u> this order?

wanted ⟶ decided ⟶ went ⟶ arrived ⟶ opened ⟶ found

Education is wasted on young people.

Traditional quotation

Do you agree with this quotation?

2B | Irish schools

Can do (tick ✓)

- [ ] I can understand the main ideas of each paragraph in a magazine article.
- [ ] I can have a discussion about schools in my town.
- [ ] I can talk about schools in my country now and in the past.
- [ ] I can use *used to* to talk about schools in my country in the past.

Schools in the past

Write about some things that used to happen in schools in your country that don't happen now.

School memories

Write about something that happened to you at school that you will always remember.

What's six times nine?

How can you teach mathematics if you don't know that?

Your day

What was your day like today? Circle the best words.

boring   funny   strange   interesting

tiring   quiet   busy   frustrating

Now write a sentence to describe your day.

_____

_____

Teachers are people who used to like children.
Anonymous

| 15

2c | Red faces

Can do (tick ✓)

- [ ] I can understand messages on an internet discussion group web page.
- [ ] I can have a discussion about parent-child relationships.
- [ ] I can describe an embarrassing experience.
- [ ] I can use the past simple and past continuous to describe a past experience.

Embarrassment-ometer

Fill in the meter to show how embarrassing each thing is for you.

Example:

0%   100%

Speaking English in class

Meeting new people

Spilling food on your clothes

Saying something stupid

Forgetting people's names

Embarrassing things I have said or done

Write a few sentences about embarrassing things you have said or done at work, in a lesson, at home or with friends.

A thinking game

Think of a famous person. Imagine what they were doing yesterday at 9.15 am / at midday / at 7 pm / at midnight.

'Yes, yes. I know it's a very important meeting. No, I haven't forgotten anything.'

2D | Which school?

Date: _____

Can do (tick✓)

 I can understand specific information in a conversation.
 I can ask for information about courses in a school.
 I can discuss the use of English in my country.
 I can combine words to make collocations.

'Now I can finally read your handwriting
I realize you can't spell.'

Diary

Look back through Units 1 and 2. What were the most important things you learnt? What was the best lesson you had?

_____

_____

_____

_____

_____

_____

_____

_____

My schooldays

Which of these statements about school do you agree with? Write your own statement about school.

My schooldays were the best days of my life.

School is just a way of keeping young people quiet.

I hated school. I never learnt a thing.

3A | Flatmates

Can do (tick ✓)

- [ ] I can understand two friends talking about their home life.
- [ ] I can ask and answer questions about my home life.
- [ ] I can discuss problems and find a solution to them.
- [ ] I can use countable and uncountable nouns to compare two pictures.

Living with your parents or living alone

What is best: living with your parents, living on your own or living with friends in a flat? Why?

Diary

What is the most interesting thing that has happened in your English class so far?

_____

_____

_____

_____

_____

_____

_____

My room

Circle the words to describe your room.

tidy   untidy   bright   clean   pleasant
comfortable   small   big   unusual   interesting
attractive   boring   peaceful   noisy

Circle the things you have in your room.

books   CDs   paper   computer   pictures
posters   clock   DVDs   table   newspapers
fridge   TV   drinks   wastepaper basket   lamp

'Hi, Mum. I don't know
how the washing machine
at college works.'

3B | Another country

Can do (tick ✓)
- [ ] I can understand how an article is structured by putting back missing sentences.
- [ ] I can have a discussion about emigrants from my country.
- [ ] I can say what I know about the United Kingdom.
- [ ] I can use *some*, *many* and *most* to talk about my life and my country.

Immigrants

Think of someone you know who was born in another country. Why did they come here? Do you think they are happy here? What might be difficult for them when they live in your country?

Living abroad

Which other country would you like to live in? Why? What might be the problems? What would you miss about your own country?

Places

Here are some mixed up place names from lesson 3B. Can you find the correct spelling?

DANCAA

WEANDLAZEN

SLEWA

EAOKR

FRADIFC

STELFAB

BOOTSN

CENYTUKK

TRONIOA

DGHREBUIN

Most of my friends ...

Write some true endings for these sentences.

Most of my friends _____.

Some of my friends _____.

Not many of my friends _____.

Most people in my country _____.

Not many people in my country _____.

3c | Home town

Can do (tick✓)

- ☐ I can use a web page to find information about places.
- ☐ I can discuss and compare towns I know.
- ☐ I can use quantifiers to talk about towns and cities.
- ☐ I can use vocabulary related to transport, accommodation, nightlife, culture and other things in towns.

Your home town

Describe your home town. Is it an interesting place? What do you like and dislike about it?

Where?

Where would you prefer to live: in a small village in the countryside, a small town by the sea or a large and busy capital city? Why?

Diary

What are your favourite web pages in English? What things are easy and what things are difficult to read?

_____
_____
_____
_____
_____
_____
_____
_____
_____
_____

Which of these quotations do you agree with the most?

❝ *East, west – home's best.* ❞

Traditional proverb

❝ *Nothing brings you down like your home town.* ❞

Steve Earle (American singer-songwriter)

3D | Lost!

Can do (tick ✓)

	I can describe a town in my country.
	I can understand and follow directions.
	I can give directions.
	I can use prepositions when giving directions.

Your journey to school or work today

What was your journey like today? Circle the best words.

crowded   fast

stressful

pleasant   delayed

quiet   relaxing

tiring

Now write a sentence to describe your journey.

_____

_____

A thought experiment

Imagine this journey: *Stand up. Go out of the building. Turn left. Walk straight ahead. Turn left again. Walk straight ahead. Turn right. Keep walking.*
Where do you come to? Which places do you walk past on your journey?

Pronunciation

Practise this tongue twister.
Can you say it with a good rhythm and lots of /tə/ sounds?

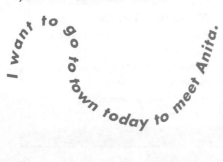

I want to go to town today to meet Anita.

'This map is useless. Everything is in the wrong place.'

4A | Online dating

Can do (tick ✓)

- [ ] I can understand a detailed written description of a person.
- [ ] I can compare and discuss advertisements.
- [ ] I can use the present simple to ask and answer questions about daily life.
- [ ] I can use adverbs of frequency to talk about how often I do things.

Perfect partner

Have you already met your perfect partner? If not, when do you think you will meet him/her? Which three words are the most important in your perfect partner?

rich   friendly   fit   energetic

happy   intelligent

kind   open   warm   hard-working

independent   handsome

strong

Find your perfect date!

Write a description of yourself for a dating web page. Say who you are, what you like doing and describe your perfect partner.

Perfectmatch.com

User name: _____   I'm: ◯ Male ◯ Female

Describe yourself

Oops!

What advice do you think the dating agency computer gave to the person who filled in this form? Check your ideas on page 64.

My perfect partner

Appearance: short, likes wearing black and white

Character: has lots of friends, makes people smile

Interests: enjoys swimming, likes fish

4B | Wedding bells

Can do (tick ✓)

- [ ] I can understand the main opinions in a magazine article.
- [ ] I can have a discussion about marriage.
- [ ] I can talk about wedding traditions in my country.
- [ ] I can use the present continuous to describe and ask questions about a picture.

the ceremony
guests
speeches
the reception
presents
the food and drink
the cost
dancing

Weddings in your country

Which of these things associated with weddings do you enjoy the most? Which are boring or the least enjoyable? Why?

'*At wedding receptions women guests cry and then drink too much, men drink too much and then cry.*'
Anonymous (UK)

Diary

You are a third of the way through *Straightforward* Pre-intermediate. How are you getting on? Do you feel your English is improving?

_____
_____
_____
_____
_____
_____
_____

Your day

How did you feel today? Circle the best words.

bored   tired   optimistic   interested   calm   angry   busy   frustrated

Now write a sentence to describe how you felt today.

_____

4c | At the movies

Can do (tick ✓)

- [ ] I can understand the main events in a description of a film.
- [ ] I can prepare and perform a short film dialogue.
- [ ] I can talk about the relationships of people I know.
- [ ] I can retell the story of a film.

Films

Which types of film do you like? What is most important in a film: the story, the music, the stars, the acting or the special effects?

comedy   thriller   science fiction   CRIME   fantasy   HORROR

western   romantic   cartoon   WAR   adventure

musical

What is your favourite film? Write the story briefly and say why you like it.

Pronunciation

How many /ɪ/ and /iː/ sounds can you find in these sentences?

Did you see this picture on the TV last week?

It's a big green ship sailing on a silver sea.

Some amazing film facts

Aliens can always speak perfect English.

The baddies always explain all the details of their plans.

Every room in London always has a view of Big Ben.

People who ride in taxis always have exactly the right money to pay.

4D | Going out

Can do (tick ✓)

- [ ] I can understand general and specific information in phone conversations.
- [ ] I can invite someone to go out and make suggestions about where to go.
- [ ] I can have a discussion about dating rules in my country.
- [ ] I can use the present simple and prepositions of time to talk about life in my country.

Going out

What would you like to do this weekend?
Circle the activities you like the most and
then make some plans for the weekend.

the theatre	a restaurant
a night club	the cinema
a sports event	stay at home

I went to a restaurant last night but the whole menu was in Italian.

Well, that's quite normal nowadays. Don't you know words like pizza and spaghetti?

It was a Chinese restaurant.

Diary

What new grammar have you learnt in Units 1–4?
Do you enjoy studying grammar?

_____
_____
_____
_____
_____
_____
_____
_____
_____
_____

Can you remember?

Which time phrases in lesson 4D go with …

1 in?   2 on?   3 at?

Look back at the grammar box on page 43 of your Student's Book to check.

5A | Tourist trail

Can do (tick ✓)

☐ I can check facts in a newspaper report.
☐ I can discuss and decide what things to take on a trip.
☐ I can use compound nouns to describe objects.
☐ I can use *going to* and the present continuous to talk about future plans.

Five places to see before you're 100

What places would you really like to visit? Why?

Diary

Have you written a diary before? How is this diary helping you to think about how you learn English?

_____

_____

_____

_____

_____

_____

_____

_____

Your last holiday

What was your last holiday like? Circle the best words.

relaxing   fun   fantastic   educational   stressful   boring   quiet   tiring

Now write a sentence to describe your last holiday.

_____

5B | Planes

Can do (tick✓)

- I can understand information in conversations at airports.
- I can make requests on a plane and respond to them.
- I can describe a journey I have been on.
- I can describe what is happening in pictures.

Pack your suitcase

Write fifteen things on the suitcase that you will take with you on your next journey.

Travel

Number these ways of travelling from the best (1) to the worst (8) for a short journey in town, and then for a very long holiday journey.

cycle	bus
car	walking
motorbike	plane
train	ship

What's the worst journey you have ever made? Describe it.

Requests

Write down three things you would like to request from other people. (You can choose famous or fictional people as well as friends and relatives. See the example.)

Who?	My request?
Marilyn Monroe	I wonder if I could borrow your diamond necklace, please?

> The world is a book, and those who do not travel read only one page.
>
> **St. Augustine**

5c | A weekend break

Hotels

List the facilities you would like to have in a hotel.

Facilities

Think about a good hotel you have stayed in. Why was it good? Have you ever stayed in a dreadful hotel? What was so bad about it?

Anagrams

How many of these hotel words can you unscramble?

FTIL   IBAMINR   STIEROECTPNI   YKE   WESHOR   UNSAA

Weather

What was the weather like today? Circle the best words.

sunny   hot   windy   cold   wet
cloudy   dry   foggy   freezing

Now write a sentence to describe today's weather.

The Swiss managed to build a lovely country around their hotels.

George Mikes (Hungarian writer)

Date: _____

5D | Holiday heaven

Can do (tick ✓)

☐ I can use a web page to find information about holidays.
☐ I can plan a visit for some friends from another country.
☐ I can use verb patterns to talk about a holiday.
☐ I can recognize silent letters in the pronunciation of words.

My plans

Write about your plans for the next year.

I plan to _____.

I'm looking forward to _____.

I don't intend to _____.

I hope I don't _____.

My dream holiday

Write about your dream holiday.

Where?	What will you do there?
When?	What do you hope won't happen?
Why?	What souvenir will you bring back?
Who with?	

Diary

What three things would you like to remember from Unit 5? Why are these things important for you?

_____

_____

_____

_____

_____

_____

6A | Junk food

Can do (tick ✓)

- I can talk about popular junk food items.
- I can check facts in a book review.
- I can discuss and plan an idea for a theme restaurant.
- I can use modifiers to talk about places to eat out in my town.

Tell the truth!

How much junk food do you eat? Do you believe it has a bad effect on your health? Do you have a 'comfort' food (something that makes you feel better when you are sad or angry)?

Feelings

How do you feel today? Have you had a good week?

> I don't feel very ...

> I feel a bit ...

Pizza time

Invent a great new pizza.

> I feel extremely ...

> I'm fairly ...

Name of pizza:

Main ingredients:

Other ingredients:

Why is it special?

'I'm on a seafood diet. I see food ... then I eat it!'

6B | Slow food

Can do (tick ✓)

- [ ] I can answer a lifestyle questionnaire.
- [ ] I can understand the main ideas in a magazine article.
- [ ] I can talk about traditional food in my country.
- [ ] I can use comparatives to talk about food in my country.

Slow food

What is your opinion of slow food? Do you eat it? Would you? Why or why not?

Diary

What kind of things do you like doing slowly? Are you learning English fast enough?

_____

_____

_____

_____

_____

_____

_____

_____

A meal you had this week

Circle the best words to describe a meal you had this week.

tasty   rushed   tasteless   relaxed

filling   delicious   boring   traditional

Now write a sentence to describe the meal.

> ### Joke
> A sandwich went into a bar and asked for a pint of beer. The barman said, 'Sorry, we don't serve food.'

_____

'*Health food makes me sick.*'

Calvin Trillin (American writer, 1935–)

6c | Coffee break

Can do (tick ✓)

- [ ] I can ask and answer questions about drinks.
- [ ] I can have a discussion about big food chains.
- [ ] I can understand the main ideas in a magazine article.
- [ ] I can use superlatives to talk about food and drink.

The best drink

Write some true endings for these sentences.

The best drink in the world is _____ because _____ .

The worst drink I ever had was _____ because _____ .

The biggest meal I ever ate was _____ .

The strangest food I ever tasted was _____ .

Cafés & restaurants

Where do you like to eat or drink in your town? Write a short description of two places.

Coffee & tea puzzle

Do you know which of these are types of coffee and which are tea?
Which one isn't used to describe coffee or tea?
Which word is a kind of coffee bean?

latte   English breakfast

lemon   cappuccino

espresso   earl grey

green   Arabica

mocha

freshly squeezed

*I think if I were a woman,
I'd wear coffee as a perfume.*

John Van Druten (film writer)

6D | Class meal

Can do (tick✓)

- [ ] I can understand general and specific information in a phone conversation.
- [ ] I can make a reservation in a restaurant.
- [ ] I can order a meal in a restaurant.
- [ ] I can use emphatic stress to correct information.

An ideal restaurant

Which of these things do you think are the most important in an ideal restaurant? Choose three.

pleasant atmosphere   excellent food   good wine

good service   music   nice décor

Write a sentence about an ideal restaurant (or a real restaurant) using some of the words above.

_____

Class meal

Have you had a class meal together? Was it (or would it be) good?

I'm sorry, the steak is off today.

Diary

What do you think about the topics in the Student's Book?
Which lessons had the most interesting topics for you?

_____
_____
_____
_____
_____
_____
_____
_____

7A | Rising stars

Can do (tick ✓)

☐ I can understand general and specific information in a radio chat show.
☐ I can describe a job.
☐ I can talk about people I know and their jobs.
☐ I can use the present perfect simple to talk about my experiences.

Stars

Which stars are often in the news in your country? Do you enjoy reading about famous people? Would you like to be famous?

Things I've done in my life

Complete these sentences about your life up to now.

I've visited _____

_____ .

I've seen _____

_____ .

I've met _____

_____ .

I've _____

_____ .

I've _____

_____ .

> You don't think this promotion has gone to your head, do you, Colin?

Things I haven't done yet

Write about some things you haven't done yet but that you would like to do in the future.

The nice thing about being a celebrity is that if you bore people, they think it's their fault.

Henry Kissinger (American diplomat)

7B | Hard work

Can do (tick✓)

☐ I can understand the main events in a magazine article.
☐ I can have a discussion about work, unemployment and salaries in my country.
☐ I can use verb collocations to talk about my experiences of work.
☐ I can describe a typical day.

Jobs

Look at the list of jobs in lesson 7B . Which ones would you enjoy doing? Which ones would you not enjoy? Why? Which are most suitable for younger people? for older people?

We pretend to work. They pretend to pay us.

Notice on a factory wall

Jobs alphabet

Can you continue this list?

artist builder chef ...

Which letters are the most difficult (or impossible)?
Is there a letter you can find six or more jobs for?

Diary

How much will knowing English help your work or help you to get a good job?

_____
_____
_____
_____
_____
_____
_____
_____

7c | Job selection

Can do (tick ✓)

- [ ] I can understand the main ideas in a magazine article.
- [ ] I can understand descriptions of people in a horoscope.
- [ ] I can have a discussion about the qualities needed for jobs.
- [ ] I can use *already* and *yet* to talk about my experiences.

Horoscope

Write a horoscope about your life tomorrow. (Then tomorrow check back to see if it was true!)

Diary

Do you feel that students in your class learn in different ways? Do you ever talk with other students about how you are studying? Do you like different kinds of activities and exercises?

_____
_____
_____
_____
_____
_____
_____

The person sitting next to me today

Circle the best words to describe the person sitting next to you at school or work today.

amusing   quiet   relaxed   stressed out

worried   talkative   boring   serious

Now write a sentence to describe him/her.

_____
_____

7D | The recruitment agency

Can do (tick ✓)

- [ ] I can understand a conversation in a recruitment agency.
- [ ] I can understand the main details of a curriculum vitae.
- [ ] I can ask for and give advice about careers.
- [ ] I can say, understand and write down email and website addresses.

My CV

What are the most impressive things on your CV? Which things would you like to improve?

Telling the truth

Is it OK to write a lie on your CV (e.g. to say that you had a higher position in a company)?
What do you think some people lie about on their CV?

Oh dear!

Would you employ the people who wrote the following on their CV or job application letter?
Why or why not?

1 I am very gud at spilling.

2 Thank you for reading my CV. I hope I will hear from you son!

3 I'm an extremely careful person and take great care never to to make mistakes.

4 I have lots of experience. I've had 25 jobs in the last two years.

8A | Futurological conference

Can do (tick ✓)

- [ ] I can understand people talking about the future.
- [ ] I can understand details of a conference programme.
- [ ] I can talk about science-fiction films.
- [ ] I can talk about a topic for 30 seconds without stopping.

The future

Write some of your predictions about life in the future. Will it be better than now? Will new technology improve things or spoil them?

Future technologies

Which of these would you most like to use in the future? Why?

instant travel to anywhere in the world

FREE MUSIC AND VIDEO DOWNLOADS

personal time travel machines

computers attached inside your brain

Contractions

Can you write a true sentence about yourself using at least three of these contractions?

'll   's   n't   've

Conferences

Have you attended any conferences?
Did you have to use any English?
Did you have any problems?

Ladies and er ... er ...

8B | Space tourists

Can do (tick ✓)

☐ I can understand specific information in a radio programme.
☐ I can describe the personal qualities of someone I know.
☐ I can form compound nouns with numbers.
☐ I can use *maybe*, *probably* and *certainly* to talk about future possibilities.

A day in space

Imagine you are going to spend a day in space.
What would you like to do there?

Diary

Do you write very often in English? What do you write?
Is writing easier or more difficult than speaking?

_____

_____

_____

_____

_____

_____

> *Space isn't remote at all. It's only an hour's
> drive away if your car could go straight upwards.*
>
> **Fred Hoyle (British astronomer)**

Thinking about your future

What things do you think will happen to you in the next ten years?

I'll probably _____.

I'll definitely _____.

Perhaps I'll _____.

8c | Help!

Can do (tick✓)

☐ I can follow instructions for sending an email.
☐ I can ask and answer questions about computers, computer games and using the internet.
☐ I can give instructions for how to use a computer programme.
☐ I can understand the vocabulary of computer actions.

Computers & me

How well do you get on with computers? Do you love them
or hate them? What are the best and worst things about PCs?

Diary

How often do you need to use English on your computer?
Do you ever use English language websites?

Thesaurus

In lesson 8c of your Student's Book you saw a thesaurus entry for *world* (earth, globe, planet).
Think of at least one word with a similar meaning for each of these words.

Verbs: select, change, connect   Nouns: order, mistake, picture

8D | Great ideas

Ideas

What is the best new idea of the last five years?

Diary

You are now two thirds of the way through *Straightforward* Pre-intermediate. How are you getting on? Do you feel your English is improving? What are you enjoying or not enjoying? What is difficult?

_____
_____
_____
_____
_____
_____
_____
_____
_____

Making mistakes

How do you feel when you make a mistake when speaking English? Do you prefer to correct yourself, to be corrected by the teacher or not to be corrected at all?

'Oh no! I think I've left the cooker on!'

9A | What's on

Can do (tick✓)

- ☐ I can understand specific information in a radio programme.
- ☐ I can have a discussion about the favourite leisure activities of people in my country.
- ☐ I can talk about what kind of entertainment I like.
- ☐ I can use -*ing* and -*ed* adjectives to give my opinion of events and places.

Diary

What films, concerts, plays or TV programmes have you seen recently? Were any of them in English?

_____
_____
_____
_____
_____
_____
_____
_____
_____

Not very frightening, is it?

Film review

Circle the words to best describe the last film you saw.

amusing   relaxing   depressing   disappointing
boring   exciting   fascinating   surprising
frightening   shocking   hilarious

Now write a sentence to describe how you felt about the film.

_____
_____

9B | Reality TV

Can do (tick ✓)

- I can understand the main ideas and find specific information in a magazine article.
- I can use the passive to describe a TV show.
- I can ask and answer questions about TV programmes.
- I can discuss and plan an idea for a TV programme.

TV quotations

Which of these quotations about TV do you like the most? Why? What is your view of TV and its effect on your life?

TV – chewing gum for the eyes.
Frank Lloyd Wright (American architect)

TV is for appearing on, not for looking at.
Noel Coward (English writer)

Television is more interesting than people.
If it were not, we would have people
standing in the corners of our rooms.
Alan Coren (English writer)

I find television very educating. Every
time somebody turns on the set, I go
into the other room and read a book.
Groucho Marx (American comedian)

Reality TV

Which reality TV programmes have you seen or heard about? What do you think of them? Would you ever participate in a reality show?

The passive

Look around your home. Write some things that were (or weren't) done last week, e.g. *The newspapers weren't recycled.*

People often <u>understand</u> the passive well but rarely <u>use</u> it! Is this true of you?

9c | Oscars and raspberries

Can do (tick✓)

- [ ] I can find a connection between two ideas in an article.
- [ ] I can ask and answer questions about films.
- [ ] I can perform a short dialogue from a film.
- [ ] I can use the past simple passive to give facts.

Oscar ceremonies

How do you feel about prize-giving ceremonies like the Oscar awards? Who would you give a Razzie to for worst film of all time, and worst actor?

The arts in your country

Write about a famous book, film or TV programme from your country. Use the past simple passive when you can.

Diary

Who in your class would you give an Oscar to?

_____
_____
_____
_____
_____
_____
_____
_____

If my film makes one person miserable, I've done my job.

Woody Allen

9D | Box office

Can do (tick ✓)

- [ ] I can pronounce dates.
- [ ] I can understand dates in a telephone conversation.
- [ ] I can understand conversations and book tickets for a show using the phone.
- [ ] I can describe an event I have been to.

Dream ticket

Have you ever seen any famous stars in concert? What were they like? Who would you most like to see in concert in the future? Why?

Write a ticket to your dream concert. Add the date and time, the price, seat number and the artist's name.

Imagine that you go to the concert – what is it like?

Dates

Write these as numbers.

1 /ˌθɜːˈtiːnθ/

2 /eɪtθ/

3 /ˈtwenti ˌθɜːd/

4 /ˈθɜːti ˌfɜːst/

Birthdays

Do you think birthdays are important? Do you remember other people's birthdays or not? Do you like other people to celebrate your birthday?

> *I'm not playing all the wrong notes. I'm playing all the right notes. But not necessarily in the right order.*
>
> **Eric Morecambe (British comedian, 1926–1984)**

10A | Animal lovers

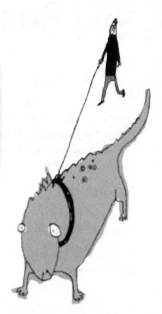

Can do (tick ✓)

- [ ] I can find reasons for a point of view in a magazine article.
- [ ] I can have a discussion about pets.
- [ ] I can ask questions to guess what someone is thinking about.
- [ ] I can use the present perfect simple to talk about how long I have done something.

Pets

Are you a 'pet' person or not? What pets have you had in your life? What pets would you like to have?

Diary

How do you remember words? Do you keep random word lists or do you organize them in some way? Is learning vocabulary easy for you?

_____
_____
_____
_____
_____
_____
_____
_____

I've lost my dog.

Why don't you put an advertisement in the newspaper?

My dog can't read!

Animals

How many animals can you find (across and down)?

S	R	S	W	A	N	D
H	A	M	S	T	E	R
B	T	U	R	T	L	E
A	N	T	B	C	A	T
T	I	G	E	R	A	D
L	I	Z	A	R	D	O
P	A	R	R	O	T	G

10B | Stress

Can do (tick ✓)

☐ I can find specific information in a magazine article.
☐ I can have a discussion about stress and what causes it.
☐ I can decide whether time phrases refer to finished time or unfinished time.
☐ I can decide if I need to use the present perfect simple or the past simple.

Feeling stressed

Do any of these situations make you feel stressed?

going to the dentist   taking an exam

flying   meeting new people

being late   shopping   interviews

Now write a sentence about the last time you felt really stressed.

_____

_____

'I wouldn't talk to Don today. He's feeling a bit stressed.'

Things you've done today

What things have you done today that you didn't do last week?

To do

☑

☐

☐

☐

Get

How many expressions with *get* can you remember from lesson 10B? Add more examples when you meet them.

get married

"Brain cells create ideas. Stress kills brain cells. Stress is not a good idea."

Frederick Saunders (American Librarian, 1807–1902)

10c | Marathon men

Can do (tick ✓)

- [ ] I can understand the main ideas in a sports news programme.
- [ ] I can have a discussion about sport in my country.
- [ ] I can talk about sports and fitness.
- [ ] I can use *been* and *gone* correctly.

Are you a sporty person?

Are you a sporty person or not? Which sports do you enjoy most? Which don't you like? Is there any sport you have never done that you would like to try?

Home-town marathon

Imagine a good route to run a marathon (42 km) around your home town (or the town where you are studying). What would be the highlights?

Did you know?

Straightforward Pre-intermediate has twelve *Did you know?* sections. Which are your favourites? Write your own *Did you know?*

Did you know?

_____
_____
_____
_____

You look at the front page of newspapers to see all the bad news. You look at the back pages to see mankind's great successes.

Anonymous

10D | Doctor, doctor

Can do (tick ✓)

- [ ] I can understand conversations at the doctor's.
- [ ] I can talk about my health and describe how I feel to a doctor.
- [ ] I can suggest solutions for common health problems.
- [ ] I can tell a 'doctor-doctor' joke.

Diary

What do you find difficult when listening to everyday conversations in English? Do you try and understand every word or do you try and get a general idea?

_____
_____
_____
_____
_____
_____
_____
_____

Feeling ill

Which of these symptoms did you have the last time you felt ill?

a headache   a cough   a temperature

Write a sentence to describe what was wrong with you and how you felt.

_____
_____

Confusing words

Which word ...

1 is someone who sees a doctor?
2 is something a doctor writes?
3 is a pain?
4 is something you swallow?
5 isn't in this lesson at all?

ache
patient
prescription
recipe
tablet

‘My doctor gave me
two weeks to live.
I hope they're in August.’

Woody Allen

11A | Things

Can do (tick ✓)

- [ ] I can understand people talking about their favourite possessions.
- [ ] I can describe a favourite possession.
- [ ] I can use paraphrasing to describe an object.
- [ ] I can use infinitives of purpose to talk about objects and what I use them for.

Diary

Think of three things that are important to you when you study English, e.g. a dictionary, a quiet room. Say why they are important and what you use them for.

_____

_____

_____

_____

_____

_____

_____

_____

_____

_____

_____

Things

What is the most fashionable thing you own?

mobile phone

TV

clothes

car

computer

food

stereo

painting

Where do you keep it?

kitchen

living room

bedroom

garage

garden

work

Classroom words

What was your classroom like today? Circle the best words.

warm   welcoming   comfortable   cold   dark
unfriendly   crowded   light

Now write a sentence to describe your classroom.

_____

To like and dislike the same things, that is indeed true friendship.

Sallust (Roman historian, 86–34BC)

11B | Fashion victim

Can do (tick ✓)

- [ ] I can understand the main ideas and check facts in a newspaper report.
- [ ] I can have a discussion about clothes.
- [ ] I can describe what someone is wearing.
- [ ] I can use modals of obligation to talk about rules where I work or study.

My clothes

What clothes are you most comfortable in? Do you like wearing smart clothes? If you had unlimited money, what clothes would you buy?

Modals of obligation

Write down a number of rules or things that are necessary in your everyday life (at home or with your friends), e.g. *I have to wear a uniform for work. I mustn't smoke in the kitchen at home.*

How many modal verbs do you know? Are they easy to use or not? What are the problems?

Clothes line

How many different clothes can you find hidden in this list?

odresskirtopjacketiejeansocksuitrainerscarfjumperaincoatmosb

> *It's always the badly-dressed people who are the most interesting.*
>
> Jean-Paul Gaultier

11c | Camden Market

Can do (tick✓)

- ☐ I can understand the main events in a magazine article.
- ☐ I can find specific information in a tourist brochure.
- ☐ I can prepare and give a short presentation.
- ☐ I can use past modals of obligation.

Markets

Where is the closest market to you? Do you go there often? What are the advantages and disadvantages of shopping in a market?

Diary

How often do you read in English? What do you find easy or difficult about reading in English?

newspaper   menu   book   magazine   catalogue

message   web page

dictionary

note   email

letter   text   instruction manual   leaflet

Things people had to do 100 years ago

Write about things people had to do and didn't have to do in the pre-technology age.

Confusing words

Do you know the meaning of all these words? Use your dictionary to check.

mall   store   chain   branch

'I always say shopping is cheaper than a psychiatrist.'

Tammy Faye Bakker (American talk show host)

11D | At the mall

Can do (tick ✓)

- I can understand specific information in a conversation in a shopping mall.
- I can ask and answer questions about shopping for clothes.
- I can ask and answer questions in a clothes shop.
- I can talk about people's clothes and how they look.

Are you a shopaholic?

Do you love shopping or loathe it? Which kind of shops do you enjoy the most? Would you rather shop in a large mall, in small local shops or at a market?

Men & women

Do you agree with the quotation? Do you think men and women are different when shopping?

> *A man will happily spend £10 to buy something that he wants worth £5. A woman will happily spend £5 to buy something that she doesn't want worth £10.*
>
> **Anonymous**

Shopping phrases

Write five shopping phrases using these words.

I'm   can   take   I'll   help   looking
me   you   excuse   I   this
it   on   just   try

12A | Around the world

Can do (tick ✓)

- [ ] I can understand specific information in a news report.
- [ ] I can describe a round-the-world trip.
- [ ] I can have a discussion about famous explorers.
- [ ] I can use prepositions of movement to describe my journey from home to school and back.

Journeys

What is the longest journey you have ever made without flying? Have you ever been on a long journey without knowing exactly where you will go or what you will do when you get there?

A big adventure

Imagine you are going on a trip around the world. Which countries will you visit? What will you do there? How long will you stay in each place? Plan your trip.

Pronunciation

How many times can you find the /ɜː/ sound in these sentences? Practise saying the sentences with good rhythm.

The girl had a pearl in her earring.

I clearly heard the purple bird.

The weather's worse, sir.

❛I see Earth! It is so beautiful!❜

Yuri Gagarin (Russian astronaut and first man in space)

12B | Let's dance

Can do (tick ✓)

- I can understand how an email is structured.
- I can ask and answer questions about festivals.
- I can describe a festival I have been to.
- I can use relative clauses to give extra information.

Festivals

What was the best festival or celebration you have ever been to?

Diary

How many emails did you receive and send today? Who were they from? Who were they to? What is good or bad about using email?

_____
_____
_____
_____
_____
_____
_____
_____
_____

Vocabulary

What words related to festivals and celebrations can you remember from lesson 12B?

'*Dance is the hidden language of the soul.*'

Martha Graham (American dancer, 1893–1991)

12c | Global English

Can do (tick ✓)

- ▢ I can understand the main ideas in a magazine article.
- ▢ I can check facts in a magazine article.
- ▢ I can understand information about languages used around the world.
- ▢ I can talk about the use of English in my town.

Words from around the world

Can you match the group of words to the language they originally came from?

1 biro   coach   paprika

2 jungle   shampoo   bungalow

3 umbrella   opera   cartoon

4 cotton   mosque   lemon

5 ballet   cuisine   mayonnaise

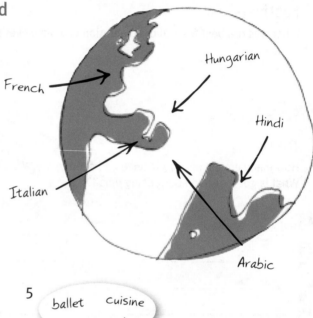

French — Hungarian — Hindi — Italian — Arabic

Do any English words come from your language? Are there words in your language that are very similar in English?

Where's the stress?

How many syllables are there in each word? Where's the main stress?

1 mountain   2 dessert   3 desert   4 business   5 dialect   6 accent

> *Every American child should grow up knowing a second language, preferably English.*
>
> **Mignon McLaughlin (*The Neurotics Notebook*, 1960)**

12D | Global issues

Agreeing & disagreeing

What ways of agreeing and disagreeing can you remember from lesson 12D? Think of a reaction to each comment.

Smoking is good for you.

The environment is in serious danger.

Charities waste money.

The UN does a good job.

Alien A: Let me land the spaceship this time!
Alien B: You must be joking. You're a terrible driver.

Diary

How confident do you feel now about your own English? What areas seem to have improved a lot? Are there any things which you don't understand very well and would like to study again?

_____

_____

_____

_____

_____

_____

_____

_____

How do you feel?

You have finished the course. Circle the adjectives that best describe how you feel about it.

happy   satisfied   frustrated   motivated   good
relieved   unhappy   excited   sorry   tired

Now write a sentence about your feelings about *Straightforward* Pre-intermediate.

_____

Can you remember?

Now that you have finished the course … how much can you remember about the characters and topics from *Straightforward* Pre-intermediate?

Don't look back at your Student's Book – see what you can remember!

1 Who did Gemma Enolengila marry in lesson 1A?
- a A Masai
- b A circus acrobat
- c A TV gardener

2 Which Canadian town was featured on the web page in lesson 3c?
- a Vancouver
- b Montreal
- c Quebec

3 In which English town did Stuart and Tony get lost in lesson 3D?
- a Manchester
- b Birmingham
- c Newcastle

4 In a picture in lesson 4D two famous people are having a phone conversation. Who are they?
- a Mozart and Marilyn Monroe
- b Kylie Minogue and Alan Titchmarsh
- c Tom Hanks and Meg Ryan

5 Which famous tourist location features in lesson 5A?
- a Big Ben
- b The Taj Mahal
- c Machu Picchu

6 What did Elvis Presley eat in the taxi on his way to see the President in lesson 6A?
- a 250g of chocolate and twelve donuts
- b four scoops of ice cream and six cookies
- c bacon and eggs

7 What was the name of the restaurant that Patrick and the others went to in lesson 6D?
- a Bella Italia
- b Parika Csarda
- c La Vie en Rose

8 What's the name of the film awards held on the same day as the Oscars (lesson 9c)?
- a Silver Vegetable Awards
- b Golden Raspberry Awards
- c Crimson Strawberry Awards

9 What clothes caused Philip Dale problems in lesson 11B?
- a trainers
- b boots
- c flip flops

10 One of the global English photos in lesson 12c is of …
- a an eye maker.
- b a teeth maker.
- c an ear maker.

My grammar now

The following grammar items have been studied in *Straightforward* Pre-intermediate. How confident do you feel about your own understanding and use of each one? (1 = I don't know this very well. 2 = I know this fairly well. 3 = I have few problems with this.)

Grammar item	For example	1	2	3
Questions with *to be*	Are you happy? Is he old?			
Questions with auxiliary verbs	Where do you live?			
How & *what* questions	How often do you fly?			
Past simple	We went to the cinema.			
Used to	She used to be a teacher.			
Past continuous	They were dancing.			
Countable & uncountable nouns with *some, any & no*	Have you got any rice?			
Some, many & most	Many Scots live abroad.			
Quantifiers	We haven't got enough milk.			
Present simple & adverbs of frequency	I usually walk to work.			
Present continuous, dynamic & stative verbs	I'm enjoying the film. I love the film.			
Prepositions of time	in a year, on Monday, at 10 a.m.			
Going to & present continuous for future plans	She's going to leave. I'm visiting there next week.			
Will for decisions	I'll get it. We'll pay.			
Modifiers	a bit hungry, extremely tired			
Comparatives	taller, more expensive			
Superlatives	the tallest, the most expensive			
Present perfect simple	She's been to China.			
Present perfect simple with *already & yet*	Have you been there yet?			
May, might & will for predictions	It might happen.			
Maybe, probably, certainly, etc. for predictions	They will certainly win.			
Present tenses in future time clauses	When she arrives …			
Passive	This was made in Ireland.			
Passive with agent	He was found by the police.			
Present perfect simple with *for & since*	I've lived here since 1999. She hasn't worked for three years.			
Present perfect simple for unfinished time	I've been on holiday twice this year.			
Present perfect simple with *been & gone*	She's gone to France. He's been to Spain.			
Infinitive of purpose	I bought it to help you.			
Modals of obligation (present time)	You must leave. She has to go.			
Modals of obligation (past time)	They had to work all day. We couldn't talk in the exam.			
Prepositions of movement	around, along, through			
Relative clauses	We saw a café that had lovely cakes.			

Now I can ...

Listening

- ☐ I can understand a description of a typical family.
- ☐ I can understand and write down telephone numbers.
- ☐ I can understand answering machine messages.
- ☐ I can understand people talking about their school days.
- ☐ I can understand and follow directions.
- ☐ I can understand the main events in a description.
- ☐ I can understand general and specific information in phone conversations.
- ☐ I can understand practical advice about how to find a job.
- ☐ I can understand and write down email and website addresses.
- ☐ I can follow instructions for sending an email.
- ☐ I can understand specific information in a conversation.
- ☐ I can understand different opinions in conversations.

Reading

- ☐ I can understand the main points in a magazine article.
- ☐ I can find specific information in a magazine article.
- ☐ I can find information in newspaper advertisements.
- ☐ I can understand the main ideas of each paragraph in an article.
- ☐ I can guess the meaning of words in an article.
- ☐ I can understand how an article is structured by putting back missing sentences.
- ☐ I can understand the main details of a curriculum vitae.
- ☐ I can understand different opinions in a magazine article.
- ☐ I can find a connection between two ideas in a magazine article.
- ☐ I can find reasons for a point of view in a magazine article.
- ☐ I can check facts in a newspaper report.
- ☐ I can understand newspaper headlines.

Speaking

- ☐ I can ask and answer questions about family and friends.
- ☐ I can describe someone in a photograph.
- ☐ I can leave a message on an answering machine.
- ☐ I can ask for information.
- ☐ I can compare the present and the past.
- ☐ I can discuss problems and find a solution to them.
- ☐ I can give directions.
- ☐ I can invite someone to go out and make suggestions about where to go.
- ☐ I can retell the main events of a story.
- ☐ I can order a meal in a restaurant.
- ☐ I can describe a job.
- ☐ I can give instructions.
- ☐ I can take part in a discussion.
- ☐ I can prepare and give a presentation.

Writing

- ☐ I can write a personal message for a website.
- ☐ I can write a story.
- ☐ I can write a tourist guide for my town.
- ☐ I can write an email to a friend giving personal news.
- ☐ I can write an email to arrange a trip.
- ☐ I can write a review of a restaurant.
- ☐ I can write a letter of application.
- ☐ I can write a note giving instructions.
- ☐ I can write a description.
- ☐ I can write a review of a film.
- ☐ I can write a story.
- ☐ I can write a composition giving opinions.

The way forward

Hopefully you will now be ready to move on to *Straightforward* Intermediate.
What else can you do to help improve your English?

Reading

- Try to read something in English every day (internet web pages, news items on news websites, magazine articles).
- Watch movies in your own language with English subtitles.

I read the following regularly ...

Listening

- Watch English movies and DVDs with English subtitles.
- Listen to radio news items on internet radio.

I listen to the following regularly ...

Writing

- Write emails and text messages to your friends in English.
- Write messages on internet forums.

I have written these things in English recently ...

Vocabulary

- Keep a vocabulary notebook. Write down interesting and useful new words that you meet when you read or listen to English.

Grammar

- Look back over the grammar in your Student's Book and test yourself.
- Practise trying to use more difficult structures when you speak English.

I practise vocabulary and grammar by ...

Goodbye!

To help you finish this Portfolio with a smile – here are a few puzzles.

A *Straightforward* puzzle

The answers to these questions can all be found in the letters of the word *STRAIGHT*.

Example: You wear this on your head.
(Answer: *hat*)

1 The opposite of left and the opposite of wrong.
2 This word means begin.
3 You do this on a chair or a seat.
4 You can see this in the sky at night.
5 You can comb this. It's on top of your head.
6 Men (and sometimes women) wear this. It has a collar and buttons at the front.

Anagrams

Rearrange the letters to make words related to body and health (lesson 10D).

1 **PRAISIN**
2 **UGHOC**
3 **CLUMES**
4 **TOATRH**
5 **MTAOHSC**

How many words?

How many English words of three letters or more can you make from the letters of this word?

EDUCATION

Example: *nice*
Target: 5 words (OK), 10 words (good), 15 words (excellent!)

Word search

Can you find ten countries from the Unit 12 Word list (across and down)?

O	G	F	R	A	N	C	E	L
G	E	R	M	A	N	Y	S	H
N	E	G	J	P	A	E	P	U
B	U	R	T	O	L	I	A	N
R	Y	E	X	L	A	T	I	G
A	H	E	J	A	P	A	N	A
Z	O	C	E	N	T	L	A	R
I	P	E	R	D	G	Y	O	Y
L	I	M	C	H	I	N	A	O

What's the topic?

These groups of words are connected with topics from the Student's Book. What are the topics?

1 float, mask, band

2 bouquet, groom, registry office

3 sorbet, caviar, sauce

4 pay rise, fired, earn

5 muscle, hormone, adrenaline

My dossier

Your dossier is a collection of the work that you have done by yourself, either in class or at home. It is a record of your level and also of the progress that you make.

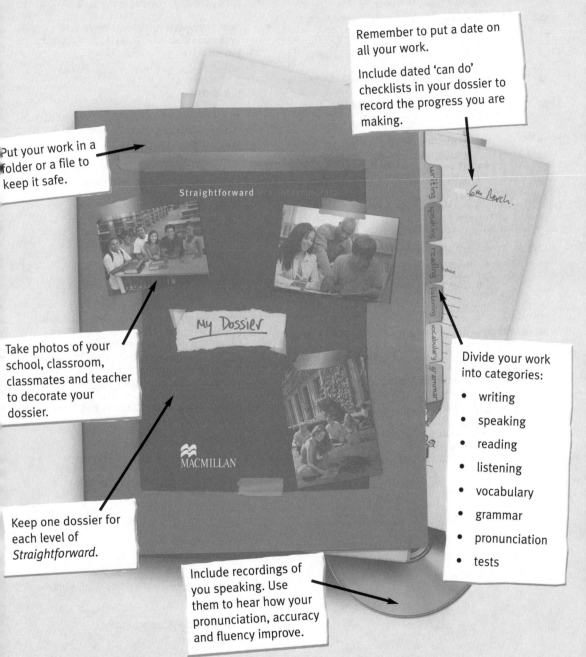

Remember to put a date on all your work.

Include dated 'can do' checklists in your dossier to record the progress you are making.

Put your work in a folder or a file to keep it safe.

Take photos of your school, classroom, classmates and teacher to decorate your dossier.

Keep one dossier for each level of *Straightforward*.

Divide your work into categories:

- writing
- speaking
- reading
- listening
- vocabulary
- grammar
- pronunciation
- tests

Include recordings of you speaking. Use them to hear how your pronunciation, accuracy and fluency improve.

You could keep two dossiers:

- a 'Working' dossier for the work you do on a day-to-day basis, and
- a 'Showcase' dossier for your most recent and best work.

Answers

1D — What was the best phone call you ever had?

3B — Canada, New Zealand, Wales, Korea, Cardiff, Belfast, Boston, Kentucky, Ontario, Edinburgh

4A — The computer said, 'Marry a penguin.'

4C — /ɪ/ is blue, /iː/ is underlined

Did you see this picture on the TV last week? It's a big green ship sailing on a silver sea.

5C — lift, mini bar, receptionist, key, shower, sauna

6C — Coffee: cappuccino, latte, espresso, mocha
Tea: earl grey, lemon, green, English breakfast
Freshly squeezed: used for juices, e.g. orange juice
Arabica is a kind of coffee bean.

7D — 1 two spelling mistakes, 2 *soon* or *son*?, 3 to to, 4 Was he sacked from every job?

8C — select: choose, pick; change: alter, transform; connect: join, link; order: sequence, rank, number; mistake: error; picture: illustration, image

9D — 1 thirteenth, 2 eighth, 3 twenty-third, 4 twenty-first

10A — Across: swan, hamster, turtle, ant, cat, tiger, lizard, parrot; Down: bat, rat, bear, dog

10D — 1 patient, 2 prescription, 3 ache, 4 tablet, 5 recipe

11B — dress, skirt, top, jacket, tie, jeans, sock(s), suit, trainer(s), scarf, jumper, raincoat

11D — Can I help you? Excuse me! I'll take this. Try it on. I'm just looking.

12A — girl, pearl, heard, purple, bird, worse, sir

12C — Words from around the world: 1 Hungarian, 2 Hindi, 3 Italian, 4 French, 5 Arabic;
Stress: 1 ●•, 2 •●, 3 ●•, 4 ●•, 5 ●••, 6 ●•

Can you remember? — 1a, 2b, 3c, 4a, 5c, 6a, 7c, 8b, 9c, 10b

Goodbye! — A *Straightforward* puzzle: 1 right, 2 start, 3 sit, 4 star, 5 hair, 6 shirt

Anagrams: 1 aspirin, 2 cough, 3 muscle, 4 throat, 5 stomach

How many words? Answers include: act, action, ate, aid, and, acute, ace, acted, cat, can't, code, cute, dine, done, don't, eat, end, neat, nice, not, note, ton, toe, tone

Word search: France, Germany, Japan, China, Brazil, Greece, Poland, Italy, Spain, Hungary

What's the topic? 1 festivals (12B), 2 weddings (4B), 3 food (6A–D), 4 work (7A–D), 5 body and health (10B–D)

Macmillan Education
Between Towns Road, Oxford OX4 3PP
A division of Macmillan Publishers Limited
Companies and representatives throughout the world

ISBN-13: 978-1-4050-9581-5
ISBN-10: 1-4050-9581-4
ISBN-13 (stapled cover): 978-0-230-02066-5
ISBN-10 (stapled cover): 0-230-02066-6

Text © Macmillan Publishers Limited 2006
Design and illustration © Macmillan Publishers Limited 2006

Text written by Jim Scrivener & Tim Bowen

First published 2006

Designed by right on the line
Illustrated by Sarah Nayler, nb illustration
Cover design by Macmillan Publishers Limited

The publishers would like to thank
Shona Rodger for her creative contribution to this portfolio.

The authors and publishers would like to thank the following for permission to reproduce their photographs: Alamy / Ablestock p27, Alamy / Comstock p29(b); Corbis / Betmann Archive p44,Corbis / Hulton Deutsch p17; Digital Vision p14(b); DK Images pp14(t), 32; Getty pp48, 54; Iconica pp12, 19, 22; Image 100 p29(t); The Image Bank p11; Masterfile p55; Photolibrary.com p26; Photonica p36; Rex / Kevin Foy p32; Stone p40

Printed and bound in the UK by Martins the Printers

2010 2009 2008 2007 2006
10 9 8 7 6 5 4 3 2 1